Dr. MacPherson eloquently lays out ten principles for Christian bioethics that are timely and courageously defended. By showing that the "culture of life" transcends the issue of abortion and is rooted in God's plan for the family, Dr. MacPherson connects the dots between the Gospel of Christ and how we then should live. Moreover, he puts us on guard against the principles of the world which are, as they always have been, perpetually at war against God and His children.

Anthony Horvath
President of Wisconsin Lutherans for Life and
Executive Director of Athanatos Christian Ministries
La Crosse, Wisconsin

Professor Ryan MacPherson's *Culture of Life: Ten Essential Principles of Christian Bioethics* is an engagingly written document that is both sensitive and sensible. Its ecumenical character and careful formulations of issues ensure that it will inform and influence persons from many denominations and backgrounds. I enthusiastically endorse it.

Professor Michael J. Crowe
Cavanaugh Professor Emeritus in the Program of Liberal Studies,
University of Notre Dame, Notre Dame, Indiana

Writing "ten principles" about anything without moralizing is a difficult and rarely accomplished task. But Dr. MacPherson does so in *The Culture of Life*. This book does not rant *against* the culture of death, but rather is *for* "promoting the culture of life" (p. 2)—centered in the Gospel of Jesus. I recommend it highly for it provides a much needed, Bible-based foundation for dealing with the issues of life.

James I. Lamb, M.Div., D.Min.
Executive Director, Lutherans For Life, Nevada, Iowa

In ten succinct principles, Dr. MacPherson expertly outlines the necessary considerations for a distinctively Christian approach to bioethics. Seeing beyond the scientific conundrums that so often cloud contemporary bioethical debates, the author focuses our attention on the Bible's enduring truths. We learn again to value life as God's gift viewed through the prism of His views and values as presented in His Word, the Bible.

The arguments of medical ethicists can seem shallow and superficial if they do not consider the spirit, soul, and personhood of *each* individual patient, not only from conception/fertilization to natural death, but even beyond death. While most books on this topic emphasize scientific rigor, *The Culture of Life* steps boldly forward to concisely examine the full picture of a person's body, mind/emotions, social relations, and spiritual nature, while at the same time revealing God's wonderful plan for each person in Christ.

As a medical doctor, I've come to understand that a person's physical health is intricately connected to their emotional/mental health, their social/relational health, *and* their spiritual health. What patients need the very most is a physician willing to care for their bodies, their souls, and their spirits. In presenting a Christ-centered vision for how each of us should treat others, from the womb to the tomb, this book turns the conversation to what really matters: God's redemptive love for the whole person.

Walt Larimore, M.D.
Medical Director, Mission Medical Clinic, Colorado Springs, Colorado

Best-selling author of *Bryson City Tales: Stories of a Doctor's First Year of Practice in the Smoky Mountains*; *10 Essentials of Happy, Healthy People: Becoming and Staying Highly Healthy*; and, *Alternative Medicine: The Christian Handbook*

The Culture of Life

Ten Essential Principles
for Christian Bioethics

Ryan C. MacPherson, Ph.D.

www.hausvater.org

The Hausvater Project

Mankato, MN

www.hausvater.org

The Culture of Life: Ten Essential Principles for Christian Bioethics, by Ryan C. MacPherson, Ph.D.

Scripture passages taken from:

The Holy Bible, New King James Version. ©1982 by Thomas Nelson, Inc. Used by permission. All rights reserved.

Lutheran Confessions quotations taken from:

Concordia Triglotta: The Symbolical Books of the Evangelical Lutheran Church, trans. F. Bente (St. Louis: Concordia, 1921), now in the public domain; and, in the case of Luther's Small Catechism, *Evangelical Lutheran Hymnary* (St. Louis: MorningStar, 1996), ©1996 by the Lutheran Synod Book Company, used by permission.

Cover art: The author's daughter "Grace" (Ephesians 2:8) holding an umbrella for her sister "Rose" (1 Thessalonians 4:14). ©2011 by Ryan and Marie MacPherson. Used by permission.

ISBN-10: 0983568103

ISBN-13: 978-0-9835681-0-0

Library of Congress Subject Headings

Bioethics

Christian Ethics

Medical Ethics—Religious Aspects—Christianity

Contents

Introduction:

There are two ways: one of life and one of death.

"There are two ways," taught the early Christians, "one of life and one of death; but a great difference between the two ways." So began the *Didache*, a discipleship tract circulated within a century or so after Christ's resurrection.

What is the way of life? The *Didache* explains: "First, you shall love the God who made you; second, your neighbor as yourself."

And what is the way of death? The *Didache* continues:

> First of all it is evil and full of curse[s]: murders, adulteries, lusts, fornications, . . . not pitying the poor man, not labouring for the afflicted, . . . murderers of children, destroyers of the handiwork of God.[1]

What the early church called the way of life and the way of death, we today refer to as the culture of life and the culture of death. Pope John Paul II popularized these terms in his 1995 encyclical *Evangelium Vitae (The Gospel of Life)*. He took his cue from Jesus' words, "I have come that they may have life, and that they may have it more abundantly" (John 10:10).

The Pope spoke in bold defense for a culture that respects life at conception, life at birth, life throughout

---

[1]*The Didache, http://www.newadvent.org/fathers/0714.htm.*

all ages, life even amid suffering, life in one's dying breath, life beyond the grave, life in Christ who has triumphed over death—yes, life in Christ who triumphs over the horrors of abortion, infanticide, genocide, senseless wars, euthanasia, and every similar evil that the great dragon, Satan, has hurled against God's people. The insights John Paul II gleaned from Scripture should be proclaimed anew to every generation. The concepts he drew forth from the experience of the church, to a lesser degree, also are worthy of our study.

This book approaches "the culture of life" from a confessional Lutheran perspective. This means directing people to Holy Scripture as the sole norm and guide for all matters of faith and practice. This book also offers guidance from the Lutheran Confessions because they properly expound those Scriptural doctrines. Theologians refer to the Lutheran Confessions of the sixteenth century as the *norma normata*, or "standardized standard," of the Christian faith. "Standardized according to what?" you may ask. The confessions have been standardized according to Holy Scripture, which is the *norma normans*, or "standardizing standard" by which we determine that the Lutheran Confessions may reliably guide our discussion.

This book proceeds, therefore, to extract from Holy Scripture, and from the Lutheran confessional writings of the sixteenth century, ten principles for Christian bioethics—ten principles for promoting a culture of life.

Principle 1:

The culture of life cherishes God's creation.

The culture of life traces its origin to the Holy and Most Blessed Trinity—Father, Son, and Holy Spirit—who said:

> "Let Us make man in Our image." . . . So God created man in His own image; in the image of God He created him; male and female He created them. (Genesis 1:26–27)

In this manner God created Adam and Eve. God is the originator of human life. The Scriptures say of our Heavenly Father that "in Him we move and live and have our being" (Acts 17:28). The Scriptures proclaim that Christ, the only begotten Son of the Father, is "the Prince of life" (Acts 3:15). The Scriptures teach that "the Spirit of God has made me, and the breath of the Almighty gives me life" (Job 33:4).

Like pottery in the potter's hands, we owe our entire existence to the Triune God. The culture of life, therefore, is a culture of humility. In the Prophet Isaiah, we read:

> Shall the potter be esteemed as the clay; for shall the thing made say of him who made it, "He did not make me"? Or shall the thing formed say of him who formed it, "He has no understanding"? (Isaiah 29:16).

Surely not! God is the potter, and we are the clay. We did not form Him. He forms us according to His will.

We are not of our own making. We are not of our own planning or design. God is our Creator, God and none other. As the Psalmist sings to the LORD, so shall we:

> For You formed my inward parts;
>> You covered me in my mother's womb.
>
> I will praise You, for I am fearfully and wonderfully
>> made;
>> Marvelous are Your works,
> And that my soul knows very well.
> My frame was not hidden from You,
>> When I was made in secret,
>> And skillfully wrought in the lowest parts of the
>> earth.
> Your eyes saw my substance, being yet unformed.
>> (Psalm 139:13–16)

God has not only brought us from non-existence into existence, but He also has brought us from death back to life. As St. Paul instructed the church at Rome:

> Or do you not know that as many of us as were baptized into Christ Jesus were baptized into His death? Therefore we were buried with Him through baptism into death, that just as Christ was raised from the dead by the glory of the Father, even so we also should walk in newness of life. (Romans 6:3–4)

And to the Christians of Corinth, the same apostle affirmed, "if anyone is in Christ, he is a new creation; old things have passed away; behold, all things have become new" (2 Corinthians 5:17).

The culture of life cherishes both God's original creation in Eden and the new creation at Calvary. The culture of life looks back to the paradise described in the first two chapters of the Bible, of which God said, "indeed it was very good" (Genesis 1:31). The culture of life looks forward to the new heaven and the new earth described in the last two chapters of the Bible, where "God will wipe away every tear from their eyes; there shall be no more death, nor sorrow, nor crying. There shall be no more pain, for the former things have passed away" (Revelation 21:4). Life is God's work. Life is God's good and perfect work.

The culture of life longs for the afterlife, but in the meantime rests contently in the assurance that God has created and also still preserves us, both body and soul. The church confesses:

> I believe that God has made me and all creatures ... and that He richly and daily provides me with food and clothing, home and family. . . ." (SC, First Article)

The culture of life does not worry about yesterday or tomorrow, but considers the lilies of the field. "Now if God so clothes the grass of the field, which today is, and tomorrow is thrown into the oven, will He not much more clothe you, O you of little faith?" (Matthew 6:30). In confidence, the church prays: "Give us this day our daily bread" (Matthew 6:11), knowing that "daily bread includes everything needed for this life" (SC, Fourth Petition).

Our lives were the LORD's to create, and they remain His to preserve. *The culture of life cherishes God's creation.*

Principle 2:

The culture of life celebrates marital procreation.

Just as the culture of life cherishes God's work of creation, so also the culture of life celebrates the special work to which God calls a husband and wife: procreation, the begetting of offspring.

The culture of life holds to what is obvious: that the one-flesh union between a man and a woman has the potential to generate the life of a child. When two persons become one flesh, a third person may come into existence. The culture of life celebrates this procreative potential that is intrinsic to the one-flesh union of a man and a woman. This natural process has a supernatural foundation. In Genesis 1:28, we learn that "God blessed them, and God said to them, 'Be fruitful and multiply; fill the earth and subdue it.'" As the Lutheran Confessions affirm:

> [Human] nature . . . is so formed by the word of God that it is fruitful not only in the beginning of the creation, but as long as this nature of our bodies will exist; just as the earth becomes fruitful by the word [in] Genesis 1:11: "Let the earth bring forth grass, yielding seed." (Ap XXIII [XI], 8)

The culture of life therefore celebrates with the psalmist, "Behold, children are a heritage from the LORD, the fruit of the womb is a reward" (Psalm 127:3). A wedding toast in the culture of life follows the pattern of Laban's family, "who blessed Rebekah and said to her: 'Our sister, may you become the mother of thousands of ten thousands; and may your descendants possess the gates of those who hate them'" (Genesis 24:60). Speaking within this culture of life, Jacob said to Joseph, "The Almighty ... will bless you with ... blessings of the breasts and of the womb" (Genesis 49:25).

In the culture of life, pregnancy is a blessing to be welcomed, not a disease to be eliminated. In the culture of life, "reproductive health care" does not mean taking a drug to prevent pregnancy or having a surgery to terminate a pregnancy; reproductive health care in the culture of life *is* reproductive *and* healthy *and* caring. In the culture of life, reproductive healthcare services *serve* all of their patients without discrimination. That means serving both mommy and her baby. Medical success is measured in the culture of life according to this standard: When a woman who is with child walks into a pregnancy clinic for treatment, we desire that both she and that child will come out alive and well.

But the culture of life is not just about babies and their mommies. The culture of life equally protects the man (together with his wife and the children whom they may bear) by preserving the man's and woman's one-flesh union within a lifelong relationship of mutual fidelity—a relationship called marriage. *The culture of life celebrates marital procreation.*

Principle 3:

The culture of life flows from marriage.

The culture of life flows from marriage as God instituted it: a lifelong union of a man and a woman that celebrates sexual complementarity, children, and chastity. The culture of life proclaims that marriage establishes and defines society, not the other way around. And marriage truly *is*—not merely is *thought* by some people to be, but rather marriage *is*—the divinely established lifelong union of a man and a woman, a union that celebrates sexual complementarity, children, and chastity.

God established marriage. "And the LORD God said, 'It is not good that man should be alone; I will make him a helper comparable to him'" (Genesis 2:18).

God declares marriage to be *lifelong*:

> And [Jesus] answered and said to them, "Have you not read that He who made them at the beginning . . . said, 'For this reason a man shall leave his father and mother and be joined to his wife, and the two shall become one flesh'? So then, they are no longer two but one flesh. Therefore what God has joined together, let not man separate." (Matthew 19:4–6)

God established marriage to *celebrate sexual complementarity*. "God created man in His own image; in the image of God He created him; male and female He created them" (Genesis 1:27). As Luther wrote in the

Smalcald Articles:

> Now, as little as [anyone has] been given the power to make a woman out of a man or a man out of a woman, or to nullify either sex, so little [has anyone] had the power to separate such creatures of God, or to forbid them from living honestly in marriage with one another. (SA III, XI, 2)

God further designed marriage to *celebrate children*. As the Prophet Malachi proclaimed, "Did He not make them one, having a remnant of the Spirit? And why one? He seeks godly offspring" (Malachi 2:15). As Luther wrote in his Large Catechism:

> [God] has instituted [marriage] before all other [estates], and therefore created man and woman separately (as is evident), not for lewdness, but that they should [legitimately] live together, be fruitful, beget children, and nourish and train them to the honor of God." (LC I, 207)

God also intends marriage to *celebrate chastity*. Again, from the Large Catechism we learn:

> [The Sixth] commandment demands not only that everyone live chastely in thought, word, and deed in his condition, that is, especially in the estate of matrimony, but also that everyone love and esteem the spouse given him by God. For where conjugal chastity is to be maintained, man and wife must by all means live together in love and harmony, that one may cherish the other from the heart and with entire fidelity. (LC I, 219)

As the Proverb advises:

> Rejoice with the wife of your youth.
> As a loving deer and a graceful doe,
>> Let her breasts satisfy you at all times;
>> And always be enraptured with her love.
> For why should you, my son, be enraptured by an
>> immoral woman,
>> And be embraced in the arms of a seductress?
>> (Proverbs 5:18b–20)

Notice, too, that Scripture does not blush to say it like it is—within marriage, a man well may find satisfaction in the breasts of his wife. As Moses described the first married couple, "They were both naked, the man and his wife, and were not ashamed" (Genesis 2:25). If we fail to see the pristine beauty of these truths, the problem is not with Scripture's presentation, but with our distorted perceptions.

The culture of life, therefore, calls upon us to renew our respect for God's gifts of chastity, children, and sexual complementarity, receiving all of these blessings wrapped up in the lifelong union of a man and a woman, the unique one-flesh bond that our Creator instituted as marriage. Nowhere but in this natural family will a child be more secure. Nothing but this natural family will provide a more stable foundation for human civilization. *The culture of life flows from marriage.*

Principle 4:

The culture of life honors parents.

The culture of life recognizes that all earthly institutions derive their proper authority from the office of fatherhood. That is why Luther explained the Fourth Commandment, "Honor your father and your mother," to mean that we also should respect other superiors, including civil government. As Luther remarked in his Large Catechism, "All authority flows and is propagated from the authority of parents" (LC I, 141).

The culture of life respects fathers for their divinely established office of leadership, provision, and protection. God calls upon and equips men to lead, provide for, and protect their wives and children. Godly husbands honor their wives as they "dwell with them with understanding" (1 Peter 3:7). A godly man provides for his household—but if he refuses, then Scripture labels him "worse than an unbeliever" (1 Timothy 5:8). Most importantly, a godly man brings up his children "in the training and admonition of the Lord" (Ephesians 6:4).

The culture of life honors the authority God has bestowed upon fathers to serve the people whom God has entrusted to their care. Abortion, says the Supreme Court of this land, is a woman's issue.[2] But pregnancy, says the culture of life, is a man's issue, for God calls

---

[2]In *Planned Parenthood v. Casey* (1992), the Supreme Court declared that neither a woman's husband nor the father of her child (if he's not her husband) has any legal right to prevent her from killing that child by method of abortion. If she is a minor, her father has very limited rights to intervene on behalf of his grandchild within her womb.

upon husbands to serve their wives as loving heads of household (Ephesians 5:25; Colossians 3:18) and to protect and provide for their children's needs.

The culture of life honors mothers for their divinely established office of bearing and nurturing the young. Solomon admonished, "Do not forsake the law of your mother" (Proverbs 1:8). Children do not outgrow this responsibility, for this command applies also "when she is old" (Proverbs 23:22). St. Paul trained Titus to exhort the older women to mentor the younger women in their important work as wives and mothers (Titus 2:1–5). As God "opens and closes wombs," He determines when to make a woman into a mother (Genesis 29:31; 1 Samuel 1:5). For those whom God blesses with the vocation of motherhood, Scripture identifies their sanctified lives as being "saved in childbearing if they continue in faith, love, and holiness, with self-control" (1 Timothy 2:15). Just as Timothy's mother Eunice and grandmother Lois nurtured him in the Christian faith, so also God employs God-fearing mothers to fulfill priestly duties within their homes (2 Timothy 1:5; cf. 1 Peter 2:9).

In, with, and under fatherhood and motherhood, God the Heavenly Father distributes His blessings of daily bread, both physical and spiritual. Amazingly, God blesses people even through inadequate earthly parents. God calls upon us, therefore, to respect the office of parenthood and to recognize, even in the quirky personalities of some parents, the divine office of parental blessings—what Luther called "a majesty there hidden" (LC I, 106). Recognizing God's special callings for both fathers and mothers, *the culture of life honors parents.*

Principle 5:

The culture of life respects the elderly.

The honor that children owe to their parents does not end when children become adults or when parents become grandparents. Nor does this honor consist of mere lip service. As Luther explains in the Large Catechism:

> We show them such honor also by works, that is, with our body and possessions, that we serve them, help them, and provide for them when they are old, sick, infirm, or poor, and all that not only gladly, but with humility and reverence, as doing it before God. For [the person] who knows how to regard them in his heart will not allow them to suffer want or hunger, but will place them above him[self] and at his side, and will share with them whatever he has and possesses. (LC I, 111)

In the culture of life, one's first reaction is not to put Grandma in a nursing home, but to open one's own home: to meet her needs, to share her burdens, and to celebrate the blessings God places in her life (cf. 2 Samuel 9). The "majesty there hidden" does not fade with age; rather, as the Proverb teaches us, "The silver-haired head is a crown of glory, if it is found in the way of righteousness" (Proverbs 16:31). True, "the glory of young men is their strength," but the Scriptures also teach that "the splendor of old men is their gray head" (Proverbs 20:29).

Let us not think lightly of the fact that Jacob blessed his children and his children's children when he was well advanced in years (Genesis 49). Young King Rehoboam, on the other hand, foolishly neglected the sage advice of his elders in favor of the youthful generation's short-sighted plans (1 Kings 12:6–15).

The culture of life respects human life at all its stages, recognizing that those who have lived long and well have much to offer those who are just beginning their journeys on this earth. Not only should the young respect the aging, but the elderly should also respect themselves with the honor God says is due them. If Grandpa is too weak to work, he is not too weak to pray. Let us cherish our parents and grandparents as they intercede on our behalf and pass down to their children's children the wisdom of the Lord.

In the face of grave illness, the culture of life acknowledges that God alone determines the length of our days. He granted King Hezekiah fifteen additional years (Isaiah 38:5). "My times," wrote the psalmist, "are in Your hand" (Psalm 31:15). Christ healed the sick, raised the dead, and proclaimed a living Gospel for this world and the next. Thus we pray, "Deliver us from evil," which Luther expounds as follows:

> We pray in this petition . . . that our Father in heaven would deliver us from every evil of body and soul . . . and at last, when the hour of death shall come, grant us a blessed end, and graciously take us from this valley of sorrow to Himself in heaven. (SC, Seventh Petition)

To protect our lives until the day that God chooses to be our last, the LORD has given the Fifth Commandment: "You shall not kill." The culture of life recognizes that "mercy killing," despite its friendly name, is *murder*; genuine mercy comforts the soul with Word and Sacrament and cares for the body as best one can. But to kill is to take away what God has given, to injure what God seeks to protect, to cut short what God has measured more abundantly than we can ask or imagine (cf. Ephesians 3:20).

When, however, God has made clear that someone's death is imminent, then the culture of life teaches an acceptance of His will. The culture of life does not seek to preserve a life that no longer can be preserved, but rather to respect both God's gift of life and God's timing for death. Life is ours to protect and cherish, but it is God's to prolong and God's to end (Deuteronomy 32:39 and Psalm 31:15).

Amid difficult situations, the culture of life remembers that neither the avoidance of suffering for oneself nor the avoidance of watching a loved one suffer should be the highest priority. Instead, the culture of life discovers comfort in the face of tragedy by recalling the redemptive purpose of Christ's suffering (Hebrews 13:12). Suffering is real. Suffering is difficult. Even so, "the sufferings of this present time are not worthy to be compared with the glory which shall be revealed in us" (Romans 8:18).

In the culture of life, therefore, we "fear and love God, so that we do no bodily harm to our neighbor, but help and befriend him in every need" (SC, Fifth Commandment). This we do for the sick as much as for the healthy, for the weak as much as for the strong, for the old as much as for the young. *The culture of life respects the elderly.*

Principle 6:

The culture of life provides for widows and orphans.

"Pure and undefiled religion before God and the Father is this: to visit orphans and widows in their trouble, and to keep oneself unspotted from the world" (James 1:27). These words from St. James remind us why "faith without works is dead" (James 2:20). God is the proper object of our faith, and God Himself is "a father of the fatherless, and a defender of widows" (Psalm 68:5). The Prophet Isaiah's appeal to Israel conveys a timeless moral imperative:

> Learn to do good;
> Seek justice,
>   Rebuke the oppressor;
> Defend the fatherless,
>   Plead for the widow. (Isaiah 1:17)

As we contemplate these words today, however, we may find new categories of helpless women and children—no longer just the widows and orphans, but also those mothers who have been rendered single by a cause just as intrusive as death: divorce. More often than death, divorce—like its common predecessor, cohabitation—disrupts the childhood of as many as half of our nation's young people, leaving them with only one biological parent in the home. To such people, the culture of life affirms with the psalmist that "God sets the solitary in families" (Psalm 68:6). God gives people their families. He preserves families. He can restore families, too.

Along the way, God calls upon all of us to support those in need. Statistics indicate that men, women, and children alike have the greatest difficulty meeting their material needs when they no longer live within the protection that marriage so uniquely provides. As citizens entrapped in a post-marital social disorder, we have all the greater responsibility to assist lonely fathers, support isolated mothers, and rescue abandoned children. Let us seek to reunite husband and wife, parent and child, helping families stitch back together the tattered fabric of their lives.

When needed, let us also open our own homes to adopt an orphan; to serve as foster parents for children who temporarily lack adequate care; or to house, feed, and encourage a lonely pregnant woman in the time of her distress. *The culture of life provides for widows and orphans.*

Principle 7:

The culture of life nurtures the rising generation.

To be pro-life means more than opposing abortion. Being pro-life means more than choosing to carry a child to term rather than end that child's life. It also matters how one nurtures a child from birth onward. God commands not only that we protect our children's lives, but also that we instruct them according to His Word. Parents are to teach their children by precept. In the Old Testament, the mandate was as follows:

> Hear, O Israel: The LORD our God, the LORD is one! You shall love the LORD your God with all your heart, with all your soul, and with all your strength. And these words which I command you today shall be in your heart. You shall teach them diligently to your children, and shall talk of them when you sit in your house, when you walk by the way, when you lie down, and when you rise up. (Deuteronomy 6:4–7)

In the New Testament, God repeats the command for parents to instruct their children. "Fathers, . . . bring [your children] up in the training and admonition of the Lord" (Ephesians 6:4). Parents—especially fathers, as the divinely appointed heads of their households—have a responsibility not only to provide for their children's bodily lives, but also to nourish, train, and protect their children's souls. As Luther admonished in the Large

Catechism:

> Let every one know, therefore, that it is his duty, on peril of losing the divine favor, to bring up his children above all things in the fear and knowledge of God, and if they are talented, have them learn and study something, that they may be employed for whatever need there is. (LC I, 173–74)

In addition to teaching by precept, parents also should teach by example. Take a child with you when you visit a sick person in the hospital. Involve your children in kitchen work when you prepare a meal for a family that has a new baby. Model for your children with your prayers how to entrust your Heavenly Father with every concern for this body and life. Proclaim, in all that you say and do, that God has given us new life in Christ Jesus. Join with the psalmist in saying of God's mercies:

> We will not hide them from [our] children,
>> Telling to the generation to come
>>> the praises of the LORD,
>> And His strength and His wonderful
>>> works that He has done. . . .
> That the generation to come might know them,
>> The children who would be born,
>> That they may arise and declare them to their
>>> children,
> That they may set their hope in God. (Psalm 78:4,6–7)

The culture of life nurtures the rising generation.

Principle 8:

The culture of life fosters a free and just society.

The culture of life respects government as a blessing from God. Scripture teaches that God establishes governments "for the punishment of evildoers and for the praise of those who do good" (1 Peter 2:14). As St. Paul explained to the Christians under Roman governance:

> For rulers are not a terror to good works, but to evil. Do you want to be unafraid of the authority? Do what is good, and you will have praise from the same. For he is God's minister to you for good. But if you do evil, be afraid; for he does not bear the sword in vain; for he is God's minister, an avenger to execute wrath on him who practices evil. (Romans 13:3–4)

The culture of life recognizes that God Himself has distinguished between ordinary citizens, whom He commands always to preserve their neighbor's lives, and civil government, whom He permits to execute duly convicted criminals. The Fifth Commandment, "You shall not kill," prohibits private individuals from seeking retribution on their own, but it does not forbid public officials from trying, convicting, sentencing, and executing those who have committed a capital offense. As Luther's Large Catechism explains:

> God and government are not included in this commandment, nor is the power to kill, which they have, taken away. For God has delegated

> His authority to punish evil-doers to the
> government. ... Therefore, what is here
> forbidden is forbidden to the individual in his
> relation to any one else, and not to the
> government. (LC I, 181)

The divinely appointed authority of the government for executing duly convicted criminals does not, however, constitute an obligation to execute them. Clemency remains a legitimate option. In such cases, mercy does not invalidate justice, but confirms it; a society recognizes mercy precisely because the government has the legitimate right to punish a wrongdoer "life ... for life" (Deuteronomy 19:21) but sometimes chooses not to do so.

Governments punish those who do wrong in order to protect those who do right. Therefore, a war waged for national defense may at times be both necessary and beneficial. The culture of life accepts this responsibility with trembling awe, recognizing that a war waged wantonly is neither necessary nor beneficial. The fact that foreign policy crafters sometimes fail to distinguish a just from an unjust war does not invalidate the legitimacy of a soldier's vocation. Like so much else in the realm of civil government, a Christian may in good conscience serve in the military. As the Augsburg Confession affirmed:

> It is right for Christians to bear civil office, to
> sit as judges, to judge matters by the Imperial
> and other existing laws, to award just
> punishments, to engage in just wars, to serve as
> soldiers, to make legal contracts, to hold
> property, to make [an] oath when required by
> the magistrates. ... (AC XVI, 2)

Laws, contracts, and other contrivances of civil government have important roles for the culture of life. The culture of life affirms that personal moral decisions are in fact *inter*personal and therefore social. Consequently, a seemingly private matter may properly fall under public jurisdiction.

So it is with one of the most prominent moral debates of our own day: abortion. The deliberate ending of an innocent life within the womb is not to be construed as a private choice, but as a public crime. To keep government out of such matters would fail to protect the weak or correct those who misuse strength. Government must, therefore, take a stand for truth and justice, seeking the preservation of life.

But when a government abuses its proper authority and requires citizens to violate God's moral law, the culture of life calls for civil disobedience in the spirit of Daniel, Shadrach, Meschach, and Abednego (Daniel 3 and 6). With St. Peter, the culture of life affirms, "We must obey God rather than men" (Acts 5:29).

Recognizing God's law as supreme, the culture of life conscientiously objects to government mandates for participation in the wrongful taking of human life. For example, the culture of life defines justice not in terms of universal access to abortion, but in terms of non-discriminatory healthcare for women and their yet-to-be-born babies. The culture of life refuses to worship at the altars of Molech, where King Manasseh burned his children alive in the Valley of Ben Hinnom (2 Kings 23:10; 2 Chronicles 33:6)

The culture of life also recognizes that Holy

Scripture calls upon Christians, both individually and corporately, to provide for widows, orphans, the poor, and the sick (Matthew 25:34–40; 2 Corinthians 8; 1 Timothy 5:3–16; James 1:27, 5:14). God's people do well to fulfill these responsibilities personally rather than delegating them to the state. Civil government, for its part, ought not mandate that Christian social service providers violate their religious creed by participating in abortion, euthanasia, or other immoral practices.

Particularly in the United States, the conscientious objector may assert a positive right to religious liberty, free speech, and free association according to the Bill of Rights. Here we follow the example of St. Paul, who made use of the civil rights available to him when saying, "I appeal to Caesar!" (Acts 25:11). *The culture of life fosters a free and just society.*

Principle 9:

The culture of life appears doomed to extinction.

The culture of life, as described thus far, may sound nice, but where can it been found? The culture we daily encounter is not a culture of life, but of death. As the *Didache* observed, "There are two ways: one of life and the other of death; but a great difference between the two ways."

In our system of perverted justice, a woman can hire someone to kill the child within her womb for any reason she chooses. The men in her life have no legal standing for securing a court order to prevent this, nor will the state punish her, or the childslayer whom she hires, if she follows through.

In the nation we call the "land of the free and the home of the brave," parents are asked to retreat back to the privacy of their homes and pastors are confined to their pulpits, while teachers are bound by public policy to instruct the youth that there is no difference between chastity and promiscuity. The culture of death stubbornly refuses to heed the well-documented medical facts that extramarital relations put participants at risk for disease and untimely death. The culture instead strives to silence the obvious truth that chastity faithfully preserves existing lives and safely procreates new lives.

The culture of death teaches the elderly to perceive themselves as burdens to others, coaching them to spend their final years in the seclusion of a nursing home or to cut those years short through physician-assisted suicide. The same culture occupies the middle generation with their own private pursuits of personal fulfillment, minimizing the time they spend with both the young and the old.

The culture of death hides behind a lot of clever slogans, such as "a woman's right to choose," "pro-choice," and "reproductive freedom." Dr. Bernard Nathanson introduced these expressions while working with the National Association for Repeal of Abortion Laws some forty years ago.[3] Despite his lip service to "choice" and "freedom," Dr. Nathanson himself was trapped in a dismal culture of death. Raised by a controlling father, he entered medical school to fulfill parental expectations and, after impregnating his girlfriend, accepted a $500 gift from his father to pay for her abortion.

"The night before the abortion," Nathanson wrote, "we slept together huddled in each other's arms; we both wept, for the baby we were about to lose, and for the love we both knew would be irreparably damaged by what we were about to do." They soon parted ways, and Nathanson married another woman, whom, he later admitted, he also did not love. After divorcing his first two wives and impregnating a new girlfriend, Dr. Nathanson performed the surgery to abort his very own child.

Then, in the wake of legalization, hospitals became overwhelmed by the demand for first-trimester

---

[3]Jennifer Taylor, "The Choice of Liberty," *H[uman] L[ife] I[nternational] Reports*, rpt. *The Catholic Exchange*, 27 May 2002, *catholicexchange.com/2002/05/27/95308*.

abortions. Dr. Nathanson therefore pioneered an outpatient procedure that would allow clinics to take over. During the 1970s, he supervised 75,000 abortions at "the biggest abortion clinic in the western world," New York's Center for Reproductive and Sexual Health. Meanwhile, his public speaking engagements in the medical and legal communities earned him the nickname "abortion king."

The power of Dr. Nathanson's pro-choice rhetoric manifested itself most strongly when he began serving as the Chief of Obstetrical Services at St. Luke's Hospital, also in New York. There he experienced the "moral whipsaw" of aborting a 23-week-old fetus at the request of one woman while trying, during the very same shift, to rescue another 23-week-old fetus for a woman who went into premature labor and wanted her baby saved. In the era of legalized abortion, personal choice had the power to determine the difference between life and death.[4]

The culture of death is, in the final analysis, a culture of deception. The serpent said to Eve long ago, "You will not surely die" (Genesis 3:4). Advocates of abortion today speak misleadingly of death as if it is life. *Roe v. Wade* (1973), the landmark Supreme Court case that forced every state in the union to permit abortion, was built on a series of unstable assumptions and at times even outright lies. Nowhere does the Constitution guarantee a right to privacy, but the Court claimed women have a constitutional right to privacy that includes the supposedly private decision to abort a child. The personality behind this case was "Jane Roe,"

[4] Bernard Nathanson, *The Hand of God: A Journey from Death to Life by the Abortion Doctor Who Changed His Mind* (New York: Regency, 1996), 56, 92, 128.

whose real name was Norma McCorvey. Whatever her name, her story of rape was fabricated by crafty attorneys seeking to win her case. Meanwhile, McCorvey herself never procured an abortion. She had never even desired one. All she requested was help amid the challenges of pregnancy and single parenting.

The culture of death offers no comfort to women in crisis, nor to the children they carry. Sadly, the assault brought against those who are vulnerable because of their youth or fertility also comes against those who are vulnerable because of their age or morbidity. The laws of several states now forbid coroners from recording "physician-assisted suicide" as a cause of death; state law requires that they instead indicate some other cause when a person enlists a medical professional to kill himself under the so-called Death with Dignity Act. Even more insidious, laws excuse from legal liability those who seek to persuade patients to ask their doctor for a death pill. Meanwhile, life-affirming physicians are forbidden by law from forming pro-life clinics that would employ only doctors who vow never to prescribe a drug for ending a patient's life.[5] The Hippocratic Oath contained such a vow: "I will give no deadly medicine to any one if asked, nor suggest any such counsel"[6]—but in several U.S. states that vow is

---

[5]Ryan C. MacPherson, "The Coercive Reality behind Pro-Choice Rhetoric: Identifying What 'Popular Sovereignty,' 'Reproductive Freedom,' and 'Death with Dignity' Demand from Persons Who Disagree,'" *Life and Learning* (Proceedings of the 2009 University Faculty for Life Conference, St. Thomas Law School, Minneapolis, MN, 5–7 June 2009) (in press), forthcoming at *www.uffl.org*.

[6]Translated by Francis Adams. Available online: *http://classics.mit.edu/Hippocrates/hippooath.html*. The authorship of this oath is in doubt, but the text was current among the disciples of Hippocrates, a Greek physician (460–377 B.C.).

now illegal, and physician-assisted suicide is the law of the land.

Well has the Prophet Isaiah spoken:

Woe to those who call evil good, and good evil;
 Who put darkness for light, and light for darkness;
 Who put bitter for sweet, and sweet for bitter!
  (Isaiah 5:20)

Woe to the world in which we live today! *The culture of life appears doomed to extinction.*

Principle 10:

The culture of life heralds the Gospel of Jesus Christ.

The culture of life does not lose hope, not even on the gloomiest of days. The culture of life stands atop the dark mountain of Calvary on Holy Friday confident that in the midst of suffering there will be healing, that in the midst of death there will be life. The culture of life prays in vigil for the first signs of dawn on Easter morning, eager to discover—and ready to proclaim to others—that Christ has triumphed over the grave.

The culture of life is the culture of baptismal regeneration. As St. Paul instructed Titus:

> When the kindness and the love of God our Savior toward man appeared, not by works of righteousness which we have done, but according to His mercy He saved us, through the washing of regeneration and renewing of the Holy Spirit, whom he poured out on us abundantly through Jesus Christ our Savior, that having been justified by His grace we should become heirs according to the hope of eternal life. (Titus 3:4–7)

It is this culture of life that transformed Norma McCorvey—the woman you know as Jane Roe—from an abortion clinic worker to a pro-life advocate and forgiven child of God. A young child was the first to make a difference—a young child who skipped and sang and played on the sidewalk outside the abortion clinic, a young child who drew pictures for McCorvey, inscribed,

"Jesus loves you, Miss Norma." As McCorvey writes at the conclusion of her autobiography, entitled *Won by Love*, "If God can forgive Norma McCorvey—*Jane Roe*—and her role in abortion, surely he can forgive you as well."[7] Therefore, I repeat here the plea I have made elsewhere before:

> If more people would read *Won by Love*, then they could understand more clearly the gracious will of God amidst one of our nation's greatest tragedies. Let's just hope they don't keep it to themselves. Christ's love, communicated in actions and not just in words, transformed America's most infamous abortion advocate into a Christian defender of purity and life. Wouldn't it be wonderful if no one could ever hear the phrase "Roe v. Wade" without remembering "Jane Roe's" repentance and Christ's forgiveness?[8]

The culture of life is the culture of repentance and forgiveness—the culture of Holy Absolution. Upon confessing our sins, "we receive absolution, or forgiveness, from the pastor or confessor as from God Himself, and in no way doubt, but firmly believe that our sins are thereby forgiven before God in heaven" (SC, Absolution).

It is this culture of life that restored a young woman to fellowship with God and with the people of God. An unwed teen, she became pregnant through fornication. But she confessed this sin to her pastor,

---

[7] Norma McCorvey, with Gary Thomas, *Won by Love* (Nashville: Thomas Nelson Publishers, 1998), 229.

[8] Ryan C. MacPherson, "How a Christian Child's Love Won Jane Roe's Heart," rev. of *Won by Love*, by Norma McCorvey, *The Hausvater Project*, Jan. 2009, *www.hausvater.org*.

who assured her of God's forgiveness in Christ. Then the pastor brought her before the congregation, announcing both her sin and her repentance. The pastor informed the congregation that he had absolved her in the name of Christ, and asked if they, too, would receive her back as their sister in Christ. From this moment onward, she experienced nothing but forgiveness for her past and assistance for her future. The culture of life has no time for gossip. The culture of life is too busy sewing booties for the baby's tiny feet, offering to cook meals for the mother, being "kind to one another, tenderhearted, forgiving one another just as God in Christ forgave you" (Ephesians 4:32).

The culture of life is the culture of the Lord's Supper, in which a person "is truly worthy and well prepared who has faith in these words, 'Given and shed for you for the remission of sins'" (SC, Lord's Supper). Whose sins? Your sins and mine. As St. John the Evangelist wrote to the early church, "If anyone sins, we have an Advocate with the Father, Jesus Christ the righteous. And He Himself is the propitiation for our sins, and not for ours only but also for the whole world" (1 John 2:1–2).

Paradoxically, the culture of life is composed entirely of people who have failed to live up to that culture's high standards. It is composed entirely of sinners like you and me. Have we sincerely respected the design of God's creation? Have we carefully preserved sexual intimacy for marriage? Have we generously welcomed children according to God's timing, and patiently accepted His will when He has chosen to withhold the gift of a child? Have we honored our parents and respected the elderly, no matter the apparent inconvenience? Have we diligently cared for the widows and orphans in our midst? Have we faithfully trained the next generation according to God's commands and promises? Have we fostered liberty and justice while also exercising civic responsibility? Instead of pointing a finger of blame at the culture around us—the culture of death that would doom the culture of life to extinction—have we acknowledged our own weakness, failure, and sin—our dire need for "daily contrition and repentance" (SC, Baptism)?

As St. Paul warned, but also comforted, the church of Corinth, so, too, let us fear God's commands but delight in His promises:

> Do you not know that the unrighteous will not inherit the kingdom of God? Do not be deceived. Neither fornicators, nor idolaters, nor adulterers, nor homosexuals, nor sodomites, nor thieves, nor covetous, nor drunkards, nor revilers, nor extortioners will inherit the kingdom of God. And such were some of you. But you were washed, but you were sanctified, but you were justified in the name of the Lord Jesus and by the Spirit of our God. (1 Corinthians 6:9–11)

Praise be to God that Dr. Bernard Nathanson—New York's infamous abortionist—came to regret his participation in the horrors of childslaughter. Ultrasound images persuaded him that life within the womb is life: a fetus visibly struggles to avoid the abortionist's scalpel and vacuum-suction tube. The "abortion king" thus became a pro-life leader, using his documentary ultrasound film, *Silent Scream*, to change the minds of others. Eventually he even came to recognize the forgiveness won for him by Christ.[9]

Are you surprised? You shouldn't be. If you know your own sin, and you know that Christ has forgiven you, then you shouldn't be surprised to learn that God can and has worked similarly in the lives of others. As God revealed to Isaiah:

> So shall My word be that goes forth from My mouth;
> It shall not return to Me void,
> But it shall accomplish what I please,
> And it shall prosper in the thing for which I sent it. (Isaiah 55:11)

Confidently we confess with St. Paul: "I am not ashamed of the gospel of Christ, for it is the power of God to salvation for everyone who believes" (Romans 1:16). *The culture of life heralds the Gospel of Jesus Christ.*

---

[9]Nathanson, *Hand of God*, 141 (*Silent Scream*), 191–96 (conversion to Christianity).

Conclusion:

The culture of life looks to Christ alone.

The culture of life is not yours; it is God's. The culture of life is not limited by your inabilities, nor can it be confined to a particular place or time. Rejoice that the culture of life is among you, but do not ever think it is yours to keep. The culture of life is, rather, for you to share.

The "culture of life," as that phrase has been described in this book, really is nothing other than the kingdom of God for which we pray in the Lord's Prayer:

Thy kingdom come.

How does God's kingdom come?

The kingdom of God comes when our heavenly Father gives us His Holy Spirit, so that by His grace we believe His holy Word and live godly lives here in time and hereafter in eternity. (SC, Second Petition)

This culture of life is the sanctified vocation of the blessed bride of Christ, whom He has generously adorned with His own robe of righteousness—the bride whom He summons to the wedding feast of the Lamb (Revelation 19:7).

For every need, in the face of every danger, when yearning for friendship, when searching for hope, when seeking forgiveness: the culture of life looks to Christ alone.

Bonus Section

God's Life-Giving Gospel Is Active at Conception

By Ryan C. MacPherson
Originally published in *Clearly Caring Magazine* (Christian Life
Resources), July/Aug. 2007.

When does human life begin? This question has perplexed our generation and divided our nation. The stakes are quite high. If a human embryo is a person, then abortion and human embryonic stem-cell research both equal murder. If an embryo is not a human person, then a woman with a crisis pregnancy has a legitimate opportunity to end that pregnancy and stem-cell researchers have a moral means for developing cures for numerous diseases. So which is it? Is an embryo a person, or a thing that has not yet become a person?

From a medical standpoint, this question has become confused by the fact that healthcare professionals commonly employ three distinct definitions of "pregnancy." Some medical texts echo the pro-life community by identifying conception as the beginning of a new human life. Pregnancy thus begins when the sperm fertilizes the egg.

Professional medical associations, however, generally identify the beginning of pregnancy with the implantation of the embryo in the uterus. This occurs about two weeks after conception, and approximately corresponds with the time that pregnancy tests begin to give accurate results. Contraception manufacturers follow this definition of "clinical pregnancy," too. The pill, the patch, the intra-uterine device (IUD), and certain other "contraceptives" should really be called "contra-implantives" (or abortifacients), since when preventing "pregnancy" they at times permit conception and then block implantation.

On the other hand, the 40-week "pregnancy" referred to by prenatal healthcare providers actually begins at the mother's last menstrual period (LMP)— two or even three weeks prior to conception. This definition is used simply for the convenience of tracking each patient's pregnancy on a standardized schedule, given that the LMP date can be so readily known. The moral debate is centered between the other two options: conception vs. implantation.

For example, even some who call themselves "pro-life" use the implantation definition, which enables them to support embryonic stem-cell research. They reason that since conception has not yet been followed up with implantation, no human person is sacrificed when the cell mass is broken up for research. This line of thinking already has been used to justify numerous kinds of birth control that interfere after conception has occurred. If the conception definition were applied rather than the implantation definition, then statistics indicate that some forms of birth control might end more human lives per year than does surgical abortion. A conception-based origin of human life also places in vitro fertilization (which commonly results in the destruction of "surplus" embryos) under the Fifth Commandment's prohibition of murder (Exodus 20:13). As stated earlier, the stakes are high.

Thankfully, God has not left his people without direction. Although medical knowledge surrounding conception was less precise in biblical times than now, it is clear that the Bible regards conception, pregnancy, and birth as a unified whole that should be honored in its procreative totality. Moses, fully aware that Jacob's son Benjamin was conceived in Paddan Aram and born in Canaan, lists Benjamin among the sons "born to Jacob in Paddan Aram" (Genesis 35:16–18,24,26b). The point is that God had blessed Jacob with that child already in Paddan Aram, where He began "knitting" him together in Rachel's womb (cf. Psalm 139:13). Throughout Scripture, conception and birth are united by God's procreative blessing (e.g. Genesis 4:1). Only a curse, such as a violently induced miscarriage (Exodus 21:22-25) or an aggressor's sword in a pregnant woman's abdomen (2 Kings 8:12; Amos 1:13), severs the natural stages of procreation.

The Bible's central message concerns Christ and the salvation He won for all people. In that Gospel proclamation we find additional support for the view that human life should be respected from the very earliest moment. Christ, who eternally has been true God, became truly human when "conceived . . . from the Holy Spirit" (Matthew 1:20). As our Lutheran Confessions state, "The Word, that is, the Son of God, took on man's nature in the womb of the blessed virgin Mary" (AC III, 1). Already then, Christ was living a holy life as the righteous substitute for those who are "sinful from the time my mother conceived me" (Psalm 51:5). Nor did Christ's prenatal atoning work go unnoticed. John the Baptist, while in the womb of Elizabeth, responded in faith to Jesus Christ, while in the womb of Mary (Luke 1:44; cf. SA III, VIII, 12).

If, in our quest for scientific precision, we try to identify a moment in the procreative process prior to which it is permissible to reverse that process—as the advocates of the implantation definition do—then we have lost sight of God's marvelous plan in predestining His people as servants in His ministry and heirs to His kingdom. God declared Abraham to be the father of many nations even before his wife conceived Isaac (Genesis 17:5,6). God chose Jacob over Esau while both were still in Rebekah's womb (Romans 9:10–13). An intra-uterine struggle between these twin siblings marked the onset of warfare between the nations they would produce (Genesis 25:22,23). God selected Isaiah and Jeremiah to be His prophets from the time their mothers conceived them (Isaiah 49:1; Jeremiah 1:5—[even "before" conception!]). God chose the embryonic Paul to be an apostle (Galatians 1:15). Moreover, all believers in Christ were predestined for salvation from the time God created the world—long before anyone's conception, implantation, or birth (Matthew 25:34).

Affirming the sanctity of human life from conception onward surely involves teaching the Law, with special emphasis on the Fifth Commandment's prohibition of murder. Let us always remember, however, that the fullest sanctity of human life is to be found in the Gospel. Christ, from His conception through His resurrection, won our salvation, forgiving even the sins we commit against the unborn. He was actively redeeming His people Israel from the moment they were conceived (Isaiah 44:24, 46:3). Indeed, God elected us for eternal life even prior to our own conceptions (Ephesians 1:4–6). Let us rejoice in, rather than tamper with, such a marvelous plan as this.

Will You Forgive Her, as God Has Forgiven Her?

By Ryan C. MacPherson
October 2011
http://www.hausvater.org/articles/245

A teenage girl stood before the congregation as her pastor made an unusual announcement and a special request. Looking at her that day, no one would have known; looking at her a few weeks later, many would have begun to suspect. She was pregnant. She was not married. What should she do now? What should her pastor do?

The End of Her Life as She Knew It

Her pastor announced to the congregation that she had confessed her sin of fornication to him and that she was now with child. He furthermore announced that she had repented of her sin. She had acknowledged her guilt. She knew that she deserved nothing—that is, nothing but condemnation. But her pastor also said more.

The pastor announced publicly to the congregation what he already had announced privately to her: that God had forgiven her of all her sins, including this one; that in Christ she is a new creation; that through the Spirit of adoption, she is God's own dear child and an heir of everlasting life in His kingdom of grace. With confidence, she could look back toward her Baptism, knowing that God has washed away all her sins. With joy, she could look forward to receiving the

Lord's Supper, knowing that Christ once and for all gave His body and blood for her redemption.

Her pastor did not stop there. He had a request as well as an announcement. "Will you, as her brothers and sisters in Christ, now also forgive her? Will you receive her back into this congregation as a fellow heir of everlasting life?" The congregation replied in the affirmative.

And that was the end of the matter, but also a new beginning.

A New Beginning

No longer did she live in fear, no longer would she wear the rags of shame. As the baby grew and she began to show, people did not whisper any of the standard inquiries: "Did you know she's pregnant?" "Which boyfriend was it?" "Doesn't she know any better?" "If my daughter ever. . . ."

In place of gossip, there would be generosity. When people spoke about her it would be to help, not to humiliate. "Let's sit next to her this Sunday." "I'm sewing some booties for the little one's feet." "I wonder if she'll need help finishing high school. Perhaps I could tutor her this summer."

Most of all, there was grace. "I'm so glad you know you are forgiven," people could tell her. "I know I need God's forgiveness for my past, too. That's really what church is all about."

The Real Meaning of Church

Unfortunately, the young man who got her

pregnant did not attend church. He did not step inside the building. Nor was he a member of the 501(c)3 organization registered as a church with the IRS. But the sad part has nothing to do with these externals and everything to do with the real meaning of church.

"The church," wrote the Lutheran reformers of the sixteenth century, "is the congregation of saints, in which the Gospel is rightly taught and the Sacraments are rightly administered" (AC VII, 1). When the pastor and the young lady met privately for confession and absolution, that was church. When the congregation gathered publicly around the same Gospel message that in Christ all our sins stand forgiven, that was church. As Luther explained (LC II, 55):

> Everything, therefore, in the Christian Church is ordered to the end that we shall daily obtain there nothing but the forgiveness of sin through the Word and Sacraments, to comfort and encourage our consciences as long as we live here. Thus, although we have sins, the grace of the Holy Ghost does not allow them to injure us, because we are in the Christian Church, where there is nothing but continuous, uninterrupted forgiveness of sin, both in that God forgives us, and in that we forgive, bear with, and help each other.

Ordinarily, the mutual forgiveness of which Luther speaks can take place quietly. "Love covers all sins" (Proverbs 10:12). Sometimes, however, the situation requires a more open corrective. "For where the sin is public, the reproof also must be public, that every one may learn to guard against it" (LC I, 284). What a joy it is when public reproof is followed by public repentance and public reconciliation!

The preceding story is true. A young lady really did confess her sin before her congregation, and they really did forgive her. This happened on the basis of what Christ Himself accomplished for her and her congregation two thousand years earlier.

As in the Church, So Also in Our Homes

Because the Christian home is the Christian church in miniature, a cycle of reproof, repentance, and reconciliation regularly takes place within godly families, just as it does among the larger family of God. When a parent pauses to help two feuding children get to the root of the matter, apologize, and forgive, that parent models for them what occurs on a grander scale in the divine service when the members of a congregation confess their sins and the pastor absolves them in the name of Christ.

Confession and absolution are the lifeblood of the Christian faith, for there we confront our sin face-to-face, and there Christ removes our sin and guilt, embracing us with His free gift of love and teaching us so to love one another. Just as parents teach their children never again to mention a sin that has been forgiven between siblings, so also the Christian congregation learns to live anew with their reconciled brothers and sisters. What a privilege parents have to herald that Gospel message in their homes, even as pastors proclaim it in their congregations. Wherever such a message is heard and believed, there the Holy Spirit grants lasting peace.

"Return to Me": The Perfect Marriage Is Founded on Forgiveness in Christ

By Marie MacPherson
October 2011
http://www.hausvater.org/articles/246

Their hands grip tightly. They gaze into each others' eyes. They faithfully promise, "I do." It is a match made in heaven—that almost wasn't made at all.

Several months earlier, the young man and woman were in love. They wanted to spend their lives together. Convinced that this was God's plan for their lives, they became engaged. As the plans for the wedding developed, for one sinful reason or another, the woman became nervous. Was he really "the one"? Did she really want to "settle down"? Had she made the "right" choice? Doubts overwhelmed her, and rather than place them in God's hands, she worried and stewed. She no longer knew how to proceed. And then, she made the wrong choice.

Still engaged, but her heart confused, she found herself pregnant, by a man not her fiancé. By a man who had no love for her. By a man who would show no commitment to her newly conceived child. Terrified and ashamed, she tried to distance herself from all those who loved her—her family, her friends, and her fiancé. She quickly broke off the engagement and ran away.

Those who held her dear, especially her husband-to-be, searched for her to no avail. She did not want to be found. She loathed herself and dreaded the wrath of the world, and of God.

After several months of anguish for both parties, word of her situation got back to her family and friends. All expected that the wedding would be called off. But this wouldn't be the case. The groom went after her. He searched until he found her. He pledged that he had not given up his engagement promise, even if she had. He still loved her, regardless of her faults. He would still marry her, and he would love her child as his own. Her guilt was forever in the past, with a glorious future awaiting her, though she deserved none of it.

As they reach around her growing belly to put rings on one another's fingers, Christ-like love abounds. The trial this couple has already endured was certainly difficult, but it is also certain not to be the last. Yet, Christ's example of His undying love for His church shines as an example for them—as for all spouses—to follow.

This story is true. I was honored to be a guest at that wedding.

Moreover, this true account also is an allegory for a greater truth. You and I, the Church, have strayed from God and prostituted ourselves to the sins of this world. "You have played the harlot with many lovers; yet return to Me" (Jeremiah 3:1). Amazingly, the One against whom we have sinned longs to forgive us. "I have blotted out, like a thick cloud, your transgressions. . . . Return to Me, for I have redeemed you" (Isaiah 44:22). No sin is too great for God to forgive. Your Savior Jesus welcomes you back to His arms, as a bride whom He Himself has made holy and pure (Ephesians 5:26–27). Because His love knows no limits, He has returned you to Himself.

How a Christian Child's Love Won Jane Roe's Heart

Norma McCorvey (with Gary Thomas), *Won by Love* (Nashville: Thomas Nelson, 1998)
Reviewed by Ryan C. MacPherson
January 22, 2009, the 36th Anniversary of *Roe v. Wade*
http://www.hausvater.org/book-reviews/152

In her own small world she was Norma McCorvey, a battered, then abandoned, wife and drug addict, pregnant but not desiring a child. The wider world would know her as "Jane Roe" of *Roe v. Wade*, the 1973 U.S. Supreme Court decision that legalized abortion nationwide. The story told there was tragic: a woman gang raped, forced into pregnancy, and denied the opportunity to terminate that pregnancy since abortion was outlawed in Texas. This story, however, was a lie—fabricated by attorney Sarah Weddington, who herself had obtained an illegal abortion and now was on a mission to make abortion available legally. When McCorvey became "Roe," she provided the tool Weddington needed to push the issue in the courts. But after McCorvey signed "Roe's" affidavit, affirming the fabricated story as her own, Weddington reneged on her promise to help McCorvey deal with her crisis pregnancy. Weddington did not even so much as telephone McCorvey until four months after the child was born.

The "Roe" of *Roe v. Wade* did not abort her baby, a child saved, ironically, by an attorney's need for a *pregnant* plaintiff in order to sue for abortion access. McCorvey had never even been inside an abortion clinic, though later she would work for one. She was both the victim of deceit and the perpetrator of deception. Marijuana helped her to cope. So did alcohol. And coarse humor, too: "I tell women we aren't killing little babies on Wednesday; they have to come in Thursday through Saturday to do it" (150). But her verbal defense mechanisms, like her lesbian relationship with an abortion clinic coworker, only took her deeper into the pit of despair and anger, a bitter mixture of relentless grief and suppressed guilt.

Even "Jane Roe" knew that abortion killed babies. While working at A Choice for Women, she tried to refer a sixth-month pregnant woman to an ob-gyn, but her supervisor insisted that the woman have access to the abortion she was seeking. Unable to cope, McCorvey had to take the afternoon off; she binge-drank for the two weeks following. Back at the clinic, she refused to be assigned to the "Parts Room," where the remains of aborted children were stored in jars for transfer to a disposal facility, after first being counted and collated to ensure that no body parts were left in their mothers' wombs following the procedure. She did, however, accept an assignment to console women afterwards, who grieved in the recovery room with confessions of having just killed their babies. No, it was not knowledge that McCorvey or her coworkers lacked; abortion clearly killed babies and devastated their mothers.

Love, not knowledge, was the missing piece in the puzzle of their fractured lives. And "God is love" (1 John 4:16). God had turned the heart of Flip Benham, an alcoholic pro-choice unbeliever, toward Himself, transforming him into a Christian pro-life pastor who joined Operation Rescue. McCorvey called him "Flip

Venom" when Operation Rescue moved into the office space next to A Choice for Women. The name-calling didn't stick, however, since no venom came from Flip's mouth. He spoke in love, as did his fellow "rescuers," including Ronda Mackie and, the most loving and lovable of all, her seven-year-old daughter Emily.

Emily played on the sidewalk in front of the two adjacent offices: her mother's Operation Rescue and McCorvey's A Choice for Women. It was a brilliant Operation Rescue strategy: cute children playing gleefully outside, testifying by their casual existence the severe reality behind the "services" provided by A Choice for Women. Emily did more than deter women from seeking abortions; she smiled and greeted, she hugged and conversed with Norma McCorvey, a woman who had given birth to three children, aborted none, and yet facilitated the abortions of many at her clinic and millions through her role as "Jane Roe." Finally, McCorvey admitted that she loved children. "Then why," asked Emily, so innocently and so gently, "are you letting the little ones die inside?" (91) Had Pastor Flip asked the question, or any other adult, McCorvey would have responded with her standard mouthful of foul obscenity. For a seven-year-old girl, however, she had no defense. "I never answered her," she later recalled. "I couldn't" (91).

In the months that followed, McCorvey became attached to Emily, and to her mother Ronda. A budding friendship bridged the gap between an Operation Rescue worker and an abortion clinic employee. McCorvey found herself, inexplicably, referring late-term clients away from A Choice for Women and toward Operation Rescue, knowing full well that since late-term abortions had the best profit margin she was sabotaging her boss's business. One day Ronda Mackie took Norma McCorvey out for lunch and mentioned that Emily had nearly been aborted. Ronda's fiancé and parents-in-law-to-be had urged the termination of an inconvenient pregnancy, back when Ronda herself was still an unbeliever.

Now the abortion question was too personalized to remain a question; the answer was clear, even to McCorvey, and made clearer still by the love of the Operation Rescue picketers, who never returned McCorvey's invectives. "I love you," echoed the voice of little Emily, a survivor of the abortion culture. "I forgive you," said Pastor Flip, himself a penitent sinner.

Americans mark January 22 as the anniversary of *Roe v. Wade*, but for "Jane Roe" the real turning point came on August 8, 1995. On that day she "renounce[d] the devil and all his works, and the sinful desires of the flesh" (187). She repented of her drug abuse, her lesbian self-defilement, her hatred toward pro-lifers, and her role in the deaths of the 35 million children aborted in America during the preceding 22 years. When Pastor Flip immersed her in the waters of Holy Baptism, she arose a new person. She had been won by love.

Her story amazes the reader, in places seeming too good to be true. But on closer inspection, it's too good to be false. Love, not hatred, changes hearts, even the hardest of hearts. The conversion narratives of Ronda Mackie and Flip Benham are encouraging enough; the redemption of "Jane Roe" into "Norma McCorvey, Christian" (177) reveals the Gospel at its brightest. But the message does not stop there; the Gospel keeps shining, as forgiveness in Christ also transforms Connie Gonzales, her former coworker and some-time lesbian partner. Remarkably, "Mary Doe" of *Doe v. Bolton*—the companion case to *Roe v. Wade*—also repented. "Doe" (Sarah Cano) joined McCorvey in March 1997 as the two women publicly identified themselves as "new creatures in Christ and children of God" while dedicating the National Memorial for Unborn Children in Chattanooga, Tennessee (236).

Forgiveness does not come easily; Christ suffered greatly and died to make it possible. "It was so hard for me to conceive that the Lord had forgiven me," acknowledges McCorvey, "especially after so many children had been killed. But He has forgiven me and restored me. And, gradually, I have learned to trust His Word more than my own feelings" (228). Though painful emotions still return, bringing with them doubts concerning God's love, McCorvey finds comfort especially in these passages: "If anyone is in Christ, he is a new creation; old things have passed away; behold, all things have become new" (2 Corinthians 5:17); "If we confess our sins, He is faithful and just to forgive us our sins and to cleanse us from all unrighteousness" (1 John 1:9).

Norma McCorvey's story concludes with words of hope. "If God can forgive Norma McCorvey—*Jane Roe*—and her role in abortion, surely he can forgive you as well" (229). Her conversion reveals not only the limitless love of Christ, but also the effectiveness of Christ's servants who "speak the truth in love" (Ephesians 4:15).

For Ronda Mackie, loving Norma McCorvey meant trusting her to watch over her daughter Emily who began regularly visiting the reception room of A

Choice for Women. Emily brought gifts of her own artwork, labeled "Jesus loves you, Miss Norma." A child's love communicated a message that anti-abortion ranting and raving, with slogans like "Abortion Stops a Beating Heart," could not. "This is what happens when Christians are willing to face their enemies and adopt the most powerful strategy ever devised—the strategy displayed by Christ's death on the cross, the strategy of laying down your life so that others, including the unborn, might live. This is what it is like to be won by love" (240).

McCorvey's autobiography calls to repentance both the abortion perpetrator and the abortion protester: the one for taking innocent life and the other for too often fighting a culture of death with a culture of hate. Either way, the world needs more people like Emily, a child spared from abortion and a spokesperson of truth in love. And to become like Emily, one first needs Christ, who did not spare Himself, but lived and died for the truth in love. Christ practiced "lifestyle witnessing" to the extreme. The gift of His Spirit empowers others to do the same.

If more people would read *Won by Love*, then they could understand more clearly the gracious will of God amidst one of our nation's greatest tragedies. Let's just hope they don't keep it to themselves. Christ's love, communicated in actions and not just in words, transformed America's most infamous abortion advocate into a Christian defender of purity and life. Wouldn't it be wonderful if no one could ever hear the phrase "Roe v. Wade" without remembering "Jane Roe's" repentance and Christ's forgiveness?

Acknowledgments

I would like to thank Anthony Horvath for organizing the conference from which this book originated: "Fault Lines: The Chasm between the Cultures of Life and Death," the 2011 Life Conference of Wisconsin Lutherans for Life, co-sponsored by the Concordia Bioethics Institute of Concordia University Wisconsin, Mequon, Wisconsin, 12 November 2011. Special thanks also are due to my mother for challenging the advice her physician gave her to abort me when she had medical complications during pregnancy; my father, for teaching me the art of public speaking and modeling for me the courage to defend the vulnerable; Rev. Robert Fleischmann of Christian Life Resources, who inspired me to become active in the pro-life movement during my high school years; the supporters of the Hausvater Project who helped to make this publication possible; and also my wife Marie, for her encouragement and love. To God alone be the glory.

Study Questions

Introduction: "There are two ways: one of life and one of death."

1. What is the difference between the "way of life" and the "way of death"? See Deuteronomy 30:15–20.

2. Give examples of these two "ways" from your own life experience. Has the world significantly changed since biblical times or do you find a lot of similarity between then and now? See 2 Kings 23:10; 2 Chronicles 33:6; Ecclesiastes 1:9.

3. Restate in your own words the distinction between *norma normans* and *norma normata*. Why is it important to keep these two straight? See Matthew 15:6 and 2 Timothy 3:16–17.

Principle 1: "The culture of life cherishes God's creation."

1. How did the culture of life originate? See Genesis 1:26–27; Acts 3:15; Job 33:4.

2. How does the origin of the culture of life differ from the origins of other "cultures"—such as ancient China, medieval England, or colonial America? *Hint*: Who made those cultures? Who established the culture of life?

3. What does it mean to be a new creation in Christ? See Romans 6:3–4 and 2 Corinthians 5:17.

4. How is it that people within the culture of life can avoid being burdened by worry? See Matthew 6:11,30.

Principle 2: "The culture of life celebrates marital procreation."

1. In what sense is the marital union a life-giving union? See Genesis 1:28, 49:25.

2. Define "reproductive healthcare" as understood within the culture of life. Compare that definition to the world's frequent misuse of that term.

3. Why is the question "when does life begin?" not the most important consideration when evaluating the ethical treatment of children within the womb? See "God's Life-Giving Gospel Is Active at Conception" in the Bonus Section of this book.

Principle 3: "The culture of life flows from marriage."

1. Identify the chief characteristics of marriage. *Hint*: Look for the *italicized* phrases in the discussion of Principle 3.

2. *For married persons*: In which aspects of marriage (see your answer to question 1) is your own marriage strongest? Humbly thank God. In which aspects is your own marriage weakest? Ask God for forgiveness, guidance, and strength.

3. Why has God reserved sexual intimacy for marriage?

4. What is the best foundation for any marriage? See "Return to Me" in the Bonus Section of this book.

Principle 4: "The culture of life honors parents."

1. What responsibilities does God assign to husbands and fathers? See 1 Peter 3:7; 1 Timothy 5:8; and Ephesians 6:4.

2. How does Supreme Court's view of fatherhood differ from the Bible's view?

3. What responsibilities does God assign to wives and mothers? See Titus 2:1–5; 2 Timothy 1:5; 1 Peter 3:1–6.

Principle 5: "The culture of life respects the elderly."

1. How does the world's attitude concerning elderly people differ from the Bible's teaching? See Proverbs 16:31, 20:29.

2. Who alone should determine when a person dies? See Deuteronomy 32:39 and Psalm 31:15.

3. What is deceptive about the phrase "mercy killing" and the term *euthanasia* (a Greek word meaning "good death")?

4. Consider how David's compassion for Mephibosheth may serve as a model for your own concern toward the disabled or elderly among you. See 2 Samuel 9.

Principle 6: "The culture of life provides for widows and orphans."

1. What is the Bible's attitude toward widows and orphans? See Isaiah 1:17 and James 1:27.

2. How can the culture of life broaden its concern for "widows and orphans" in response to the prevalence today of cohabitation and divorce?

Principle 7: "The culture of life nurtures the rising generation."

1. What is the chief spiritual duty of fathers, and how should this be exercised? See Deuteronomy 6:4–7 and Ephesians 6:4.

2. What are some specific ways parents can model the culture of life for their children? Can you think of examples beyond those mentioned in this book?

Principle 8: "The culture of life fosters a free and just society."

1. What two main responsibilities has God assigned to the civil government? See Romans 13:3–4.

2. Is capital punishment a wrongful taking of human life? Explain.

3. Is it moral for a Christian to serve in the armed forces? Explain. See Matthew 8:5–13 and Luke 3:7–14.

4. Should citizens be free from state regulations to exercise personal choice in all matters? Explain with examples.

5. What are the limits of proper government authority? See Daniel 3 and 6, and Acts 5:29.

Principle 9: "The culture of life appears doomed to extinction."

1. What are the defining features of the culture of death?

2. How did Dr. Nathanson's life exemplify the culture of death?

3. In what sense is the culture of death ultimately a culture of deception? See Genesis 3:4 and Isaiah 5:20.

4. How does the case of "Jane Roe" reveal that deception is foundational to the culture of death?

Principle 10: "The culture of life heralds the Gospel of Jesus Christ."

1. What relevance does Baptism have in establishing the culture of life? See Titus 3:4–7.

2. How does Norma McCorvey's transformation illustrate the power of God in fostering the culture of life?

3. How does little Emily's example encourage your own compassion toward those entrapped by the culture of death? See "How a Christian Child's Love Won Jane Roe's Heart" in the Bonus Section of this book.

4. Agree or disagree: Confession and Absolution are foundational to maintaining the culture of life. See John 20:19–23 and also "Will You Forgive Her as God Has Forgiven Her?" in the Bonus Section of this book.

5. What role does the Lord's Supper play in nourishing the culture of life? See Matthew 26:26–28.

6. What kind of people compose the culture of life? Are they innocent—or forgiven? Are they perfect—or yet-to-be perfected?

7. What changed Dr. Nathanson's mind, and who changed his heart?

Conclusion: "The culture of life looks to Christ alone."

1. To whom does the culture of life belong?

2. With what does Christ clothe His bride the church, and how?

3. How is the culture of life invigorated by the recognition that God provides every need of body and soul?

4. Identify some ways that you can share what you have learned in this book with other people.

Recommended Resources

As always, read with discernment and look to Holy Scripture as the ultimate standard. The following materials, although not fully agreeing with each other on every detail, will prove helpful in developing a fuller understanding of Christian bioethics.

Richard C. Eyer, *Holy People, Holy Lives: Law and Gospel in Bioethics* (2000)

Norma McCorvey, *Won by Love* (1998)

Bernard Nathanson, *The Hand of God* (1996)

John Paul II, *Evangelium Vitae: The Gospel of Life* (1995)

Ryan C. MacPherson, "The Coercive Reality behind Pro-Choice Rhetoric" (2009), forthcoming at *www.uffl.org*.

Ryan C. MacPherson, "The Natural Law of the Family," chap. 11 in *Natural Law: A Lutheran Reappraisal*, ed. Robert C. Baker (2011)

Christian Life Resources
www.christianliferesources.com

Lutherans for Life
www.lutheransforlife.org

The Hausvater Project
www.hausvater.org

University Faculty for Life
www.uffl.org

Scripture Index

Lutheran Confessions Index

The Lutheran Confessions consist of several sixteenth-century documents, some of which were quoted previously, that were collected in the *Book of Concord* (1580). By subscribing to them, Lutherans affirm that these documents correctly set forth the teachings of Holy Scripture.

General Index

About the Hausvater Project

The Hausvater Project is a nonprofit organization, founded in 2008, that promotes a biblical vision for family, church, and society in the spirit of the Lutheran confessions.

The organization seeks to equip Christian men and women for distinctive and complementary vocations in family, church, and society, by fostering research and education in light of Holy Scripture as proclaimed by the Lutheran Confessions.

For more information, visit:

www.hausvater.org

Contact:

info@hausvater.org

www.hausvater.org/contact

Follow us:

www.facebook.com/hausvaterproject

www.twitter.com/hausvater

About the Author / Speaking Engagements

Dr. Ryan C. MacPherson (Ph.D., University of Notre Dame) is a homeschool parent who has taught both children's Sunday school and adult Bible classes. He presently serves as chair of the History Department at Bethany Lutheran College and also is the founding president of the Hausvater Project, a nonprofit organization promoting a biblical vision for family, church, and society in the spirit of the Lutheran confessions. His publications include *Telling the Next Generation: The Evangelical Lutheran Synod's Vision for Christian Education, 1918–2011 and Beyond* (managing editor, 2011) and *Studying Luther's Large Catechism: A Workbook for Christian Discipleship* (2012).

Dr. MacPherson is a nationally featured speaker for religious organizations, academic associations, and public policy forums. He is a member of the Lutherans for Life speakers bureau and also has been interviewed on Pastor Todd Wilken's "Issues, Etc." radio program. Dr. MacPherson's expertise includes Christian education, religion and politics, religion and science, bioethics, and the family in public policy.

For more information, visit:

www.ryancmacpherson.com

To schedule Dr. MacPherson for a speaking engagement:

www.ryancmacpherson.com/contact

Follow Dr. MacPherson online:

www.facebook.com/ryancmacphersonphd

www.linkedin.com/in/ryancmacpherson

www.twitter.com/ryancmacpherson

Also Published by the Hausvater Project

Studying Luther's Large Catechism:
A Workbook for Christian Discipleship

Studying Luther's
Large Catechism
A Workbook for
Christian Discipleship

M L

Ryan C. MacPherson, Ph.D.

Always beginning with prayer and concluding with song, the twelve lessons in this study book provide biblical instruction concerning:

- The Ten Commandments
- Holy Baptism
- The Apostles' Creed
- The Lord's Supper
- The Lord's Prayer
- Confession & Absolution

"The Large Catechism is Luther at his best! Pithy, earthy, and to the point: Luther brings the teachings of the Christian faith into the home and workplace of the Christian. Dr. MacPherson's study questions carry the Large Catechism into the lives of twenty-first-century Christians."

Pastor Tony Pittenger, Port Orchard, Washington

"This study book meets a critical need for both parishes and homes, and satisfies a desire for practical application of the Bible in a Christian's daily life. It illustrates the great value of Luther's Catechism for every Lutheran, and indeed, for every Christian."

Pastor Jesse Jacobsen, The Dalles, Oregon

Martin Luther wrote his Small and Large Catechisms to assist pastors and parents in the Christian education of children. His catechisms were shorter and simpler than previous catechisms, because Luther wanted to focus on the basic doctrines of Scripture in a way that young children could easily comprehend and remember.

As summaries of God's Word, also containing many direct quotations from Holy Scripture, the catechisms bring to their readers the same blessings that God's Word offers. That is why Luther impressed upon fathers the importance of teaching the catechism in the home. . . .

The *First Commandment* requires that we trust in the one true God for every need of body and soul; it commands faith. Since "without faith it is impossible to please God" (Hebrews 11:6), all other commandments are contained within the First Commandment. . . .

As we pray for God to grant us the ability to fulfill our vocations, we also recognize our many failures. We find comfort only in Christ, who obeyed every commandment on our behalf. . . .

God has issued the Ten Commandments out of love. As our loving Father, He seeks to protect people's lives by the *Fifth Commandment*. That commandment forbids any thought, word, or action that would harm our neighbor, and requires that our thoughts, words, and actions promote our neighbor's physical well-being. Civil government, however, may rightfully act as God's representative on earth to punish a capital offender by execution. Aside from that special circumstance, of course, civil government should promote and defend its citizens' lives, just as all citizens also should do according to their vocations.

In the *Sixth Commandment*, God protects marriage and the family. God created us male and female and instituted marriage as the proper vocation for the one-flesh union. Marriage, therefore, is the divinely established vocation for bearing and raising children. Although God calls some people to a vocation of life-long celibacy, no one has the authority to forbid marriage, nor should anyone claim that those who remain celibate are holier than those who marry. Whether married or not, all people have a responsibility to promote chastity and defend marriage through their thoughts, words, and actions. . . .

After studying the Ten Commandments, it becomes clear that our theology cannot end here. The Ten Commandments reveal a disturbing gap between God's holiness and our own wicked thoughts, words, and actions. To study the Ten Commandments alone, we would be left with God's threatened wrath overshadowing His promised salvation. Luther therefore directs us back to the whole of Scripture, where we find not only the Law that convicts us of sin, but also the Gospel that reveals our Savior, Jesus Christ. The remainder of Luther's Large Catechism focuses on that comforting Gospel of forgiveness, as encapsulated in the Apostles' Creed, the Lord's Prayer, Holy Baptism, and the Lord's Supper. . . .

Two words within the Creed deserve special attention, since they can so easily be misunderstood. First, in calling Jesus Christ our "Lord" we do not primarily have in mind that we owe our obedience to

Him (although that also is true). Rather, we especially wish to emphasize that Christ is our great protector who has defeated Satan on our behalf and continues to keep us safe for all eternity. Second, in speaking of the Christian "church" we do not primarily have in mind the external institution, but rather the gathering of people's hearts around the Word and Sacraments, through which means the Holy Spirit creates and strengthens their faith in Jesus Christ as the one true Savior. . . .

God the Father graciously forgives our sins for the sake of Jesus Christ, whose life, death, and resurrection accomplished our salvation. God the Holy Spirit distributes the benefits of this salvation to us through the Means of Grace. *Absolution* is one of these means. Like the preached Word, it proclaims that our sins are forgiven. Like the sacramental Word, it communicates the Gospel message in a tangible way. Absolution means that an earthly representative of God—usually a pastor—forgives us by the command and in the stead of God. Absolution provides specific comfort to individuals who feel burdened by, and therefore verbally confess, particular sins that have vexed them. Absolution speaks pure grace; it does not attach conditions or demand works of merit, but simply comforts the sin-sick soul with the Gospel: that Christ alone has fully atoned for all sins, period.

Purified by Word and Sacrament, and refreshed by Holy Absolution, Christians walk forth in newness of life. Through their vocations, Christians serve their neighbors in thanksgiving to God their Savior. Through daily prayer, they seek God's blessings constantly, both for themselves and for others in their midst. Having been forgiven much, they eagerly go forth to forgive others.

Ordering Information

The Culture of Life is available for individual purchase at Amazon.com and other reputable booksellers. The author receives no royalties; all net proceeds support the nonprofit mission of the Hausvater Project.

Significant price discounts are available for bulk orders by churches and schools.

For further information:

info@hausvater.org

www.hausvater.org/books